Three Stories About
'Walking Together'

Featuring the Poplar Family
learning the language of Focusing.

Written by Sandy Jahmi Burg
Illustrated by Aaron Staengl, Nomi Miller &
Molly Guterriez

Smartview Stories™

D1600400

First Published in USA in 2022
by Smartview Stories
www.smartviewstories.com

Editor: Inge Smith Terrill
Map Design: Renee La Roi
Cover Design: Aaron Staengl

Book 2
Flesch-Kincaid Reading Levels
Three Stories: Grade 3
Supplemental Pages: Grades 4-6

The characters and events portrayed in this book are fictitious and based on real life experiences. There is an understanding that human beings are living processes.

9 781737 632412

Smartview Stories is a self-empowerment book project for children and adults ages 9-99. Here, our inner world comes to life.

You might be attracted to this series IF:

You enjoy books that have characters in them who are easy to make friends with and love.

You would like to share these with a child who has a hard time expressing what they are feeling inside.

You teach emotional literacy and want to share this with students.

You have an active inner world you'd like to explore and understand better.

You want to improve your relational skills with yourself, others, or your environment.

You are interested in community living.

You are interested in learning Focusing skills.

You want to bring more understanding and compassion to your own inner world.

You have a fondness for the Blue Ridge Mountains.

Dedication

Smartview Stories honor the creative potential within each of us yearning to be expressed.

Smartview Stories project is evolving.

I am expecting this series to practice what it teaches. It will adapt and evolve. And wow, we have two significant changes already. A warm welcome to Aaron Staengl. He is taking over for Molly as our illustrator for the people in our stories. Bringing characters alive is no simple task. I appreciate both artists being here to move this project to its next phase. In addition, I have learned some software that allows me to design the inner layout myself. This will save us time and it brought some changes to our layout.

I'd like to invite you all to email me through the contact page of our website if you have questions, suggestions, connections or just want to say hello! If you would like to hear about new books as they come out, you can sign up for my newsletter on the website, like our Smartview Stories facebook page or join the Floyd Focusing facebook group. Locally, these books are available at The Floyd Country Store. Online, you can order from Amazon and soon, from Ingram Sparks and The Focusing Institute.

In honor and appreciation of our connection here, Sandy

www.smartviewstories.com
www.facebook.com/smartviewstories
www.facebook.com/groups/floydfocusing/

Table of Contents

Foreword

No one teaches us how to live in a body. Wouldn't it be helpful to know the best way to use our brain? Could it be that we are born with an internal instruction manual? Might it be hidden inside each of us from birth? Within a language that many people overlook?

Welcome to Smartview Stories, a self-empowerment book project for children and adults ages 9-99! Our emotional literacy stories help unlock this instruction manual and its hidden language. Our body and brain are always wanting our well-being. We can learn their language. Body sensations, emotions, images, thoughts and gestures are all ways our body uses to communicate with us. This language reveals what is going on inside of us and around us. Over time, with practice, a mutual trust develops within us. We see our life with fresh eyes. New possibilities emerge.

Our setting is Smartview Village. We base it on a lovely Appalachian tourist spot called Smart View Recreation Area along the Blue Ridge Parkway near Floyd, VA, USA. We invite you to visit this Recreation Area some time to experience for yourself the land we write about. This is public land. No one lives here right now.

There are communities similar to Smartview Village in the Floyd area. Visiting Smart View Recreation Area, you will understand what a magical place this would be to deepen your relationship with yourself, with others, with nature, and with all the world.

Our stories begin in 2018 when a group of people gather at the local library to find a way forward. All around them, they are experiencing cultural norms falling apart. It confuses them. Changing their habits is not easy. Changing their beliefs seems even harder. What is clear is that they can help each other. Staying together as a community brings a sense of safety. They can lean on each other.

Four colorful families commit that day to create a fun and safe place to improve their skills at navigating life situations of all kinds. One family offers to share the land they live on. Within a year, the other three families build small homes on this land. They come with jobs, hobbies and pets. All share skills they have learned. Somehow, they do things slower yet, get more done. Families pause a lot to help each other. Each person practices listening to their own inner knowing. They practice listening to nature and the world around them. The way they live changes. These families recognize the value of sharing their stories.

From the greatest joys to the deepest shames, our characters practice the power of the pause. During that pause, they listen within themselves. Turning within becomes a fascinating journey as they learn to speak this unfamiliar language. Some of our families are more experienced than others. They all start from where they are. Neuroscience tells us that our brains are more complex than the entire universe yet discovered. It is with this understanding that our journey begins. What a ride this will be!

Meet Our Inner Companions!

These three aspects of being human help us experience and live our life. They are with us at every moment. As we become more aware of them, we understand HOW to better support ourselves, and those around us, in all types of life situations. May this trio of inner companions inspire you in your journey toward thriving.

Hummah!

[HUMM-ahh]
This female
companion is
always monitoring
our environment for
us. She gives us access to
all of our body senses:
vision, sound, taste, smell, intuition
(gut sense), touch and overall body wisdom.
Hummah is fluid and flexible, a skilled
shape-shifter. She is comfortable in the dark
and okay with the unknown.

She is capable of broad, sustained alertness
in ways of "being". Hummah says "I am your
body". She helps us explore, create,
connect, and relate with the world. Hummah
is so wired to connect that it can be hard for
her to say no. Yet, when our experiences do
not feel safe, she may choose to withdraw.
Dance, art, music, sports, nature, and
metaphor are some of her favorite activities.
She is content to pursue these passionately
with no sense of purpose. Hummah enjoys
reading people's eyes. She often can tell
how real someone's words are this way.

BEING is a way to remember Hummah.

Sleuthin! [Slu-THINN] This male companion helps us access all that we have learned about being a human on this planet. He loves to separate and label things, solve problems and find missing pieces. He is always engaged in some purpose, enjoys helping others and is efficient in routine situations.

Sleuthin prefers and defends what he knows! When things are under control, he is happy! Sometimes he worries about the future. And boy, does Sleuthin like to talk! He has access to our language center and can fire off endless repetitive thoughts when he does not feel heard. A valuable awareness is that Sleuthin tends to ignore what he does not understand.

Sleuthin says "I have a body" and has lots of ideas to keep it busy.

DOING is a way to remember Sleuthin.

Ashamaya!
[AH-sha-my-ya]
Through the
power of the
Pause, this
unisex companion

helps us claim our human birthright powers as wizards of love, time, and space. The emphasis here is on process, we are forever in flux. Change ruffles no feathers here! Embodying trust, anything is possible.

Ashamaya understands that everything belongs. Everything. The owl's eyes takes in an expansive mountain ridge view while its wings open wide to hold whatever is here right now with tenderness. No worry or fear is too big for the wings of Ashamaya. This creature can hold the entire planet when needed. It is the quality of the space that Ashamaya creates that sets a tone of cooperation, teamwork and trust in life's forward flow. We are in this together; the owl reminds us again and again. When we pause, open our wings with both kindness and clarity, we allow ourselves to grow toward our highest potential.

BEING WITH is a way to remember Ashamaya.

It's Story Time!

Hello, my Companions! Come, come as you are. Let's gather around. Find a comfortable spot.

Ashamaya fluffs its wings out to each side. Hummah takes a seat on one side. Sleuthin follows. The owl waits as they settle in.

Ashamaya smiles and then speaks. "It is time to help Smartview Village tell another set of Focusing stories. Our mission for this book involves the experience of walking together. I wonder what comes for each of you when you hear the phrase 'Walking Together'."

Sleuthin starts. "What comes is this Helen Keller quote, 'Walking with a friend in the dark is better than walking alone in the light.' I remember this because I am not too keen on walking in the dark. Safety or surprises are my concerns. Walking together probably brings talking together. I LOVE a friendly talk."

The owl laughs. "Wow, you are already very much tapped into this book. Bravo buddy! How about you, Hummah?"

Hummah steps back and moves her arms with a sense of rhythm. "Walking together is like a dance. You take a step and I step in rhythm with you. Walking together is double the sensory power. What I do not hear, my partner might and bring this to my awareness. We might hold hands. I LOVE holding hands." Hummah brings two of her own arms together to hold each other. Another arm reaches out to Sleuthin. He shakes his head no.

Ashamaya grins. "Wonderful! I appreciate what you are bringing as well, Hummah! You both will enjoy supporting these stories with your natural skills. Where you can work together, our characters will learn so much from walking together." The owl raises its eyebrows and looks at them both expectantly.

Hummah tilts her head with a doubting look. "Are we done Ashamaya?"

Sleuthin's eyes narrow. "No, there must be something more."

Sleuthin looks at Hummah. "Listening to Hummah describe walking together as a dance brings a whole different felt sense now for me. Who is leading? Who is following? Who sets the pace? I like to know these things. Without clarity, I will be uncomfortable. If we fall or get lost, will it be my fault? Ugh. I might get frustrated and angry."

Ashamaya meets Sleuthin's gaze. "Ah, you might get frustrated and angry. That is ok. You like to know things Sleuthin. I hear how responsible you try to be. These are valuable feelings and thoughts to bring up now. Our friends at Smartview Village will encounter these same things. I wonder what you already know that is helpful in these situations."

Sleuthin looks at Hummah and sighs. "I want to remember that I am not alone. I do not have to figure it all out. You two are always here with me."

The owl begins walking slowly in place, rocking from one foot to another. Hummah and Sleuthin join in. "Walking together, we are. Ready for falls or fails. Thank you both so much for this," says the owl. "We are ready. A deliciously ripe time for adventure!"

Quiet Like a Deer

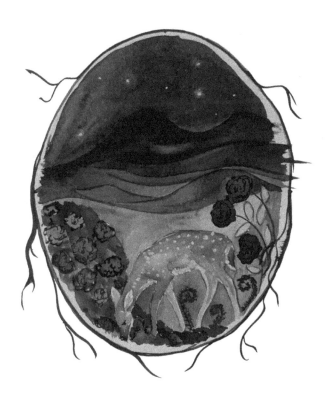

"Psst... Wendy, are you awake?" whispers Stryder.

"Yes," Wendy whispers back, "for about five minutes. What is going on?"

Stryder walks over to her bedroom window. "Remember when Mama said she wished she knew **when** the deer were in the yard eating her flowers?"

Wendy nods. "Ahh... yes, I remember." Then she squints her face doubting. "And you checked?"

Stryder smiles. "Yes, I checked within. Something woke me up to tell me the deer are here now."

Wendy continues squinting and shakes her head. "Whoa! It's perfectly quiet outside. Who would imagine deer are here **now** at 3:30 am? Oh, Stryder, something in me doubts this very much."

Stryder replies, "Yea, I heard something in me say ignore this and go back to sleep." Pausing, he adds firmly, "I am choosing to check it out."

Wendy leaps out of bed to join Stryder at the window. "I feel how clear you are. I am curious now too."

Ashamaya holds space for the whole of a situation, listening to both Hummah and Sleuthin's point of view. The situation can feel stuck if Stryder agrees with one side without acknowledging the other point of view. Let's see where this goes…

22

Wendy looks out the window. "Oh, my, it's too dark to see into the yard. It's pure black. The only grey shade is the sky."

Stryder reaches for Wendy's hand. "Let's go out there! Then we'll know." Together, they tiptoe into the hall and across the kitchen floor. Stryder opens the back door. Still holding hands, they step out into the backyard.

For a moment, Stryder and Wendy stand by the house. They pause and invite all of their senses to help them now. First, they notice the light breeze on their skin. It feels comforting.

You might pause here and see if you can
sense air on your skin.

You might notice if the air is still or
moving where you are.

Maybe the air feels cool or warm.

Always our body is paying attention even
when we are not aware it is.

Their eyes are alert. They scan out into the yard. It is dark, like a cave. They barely see six feet out.

Wendy whispers, "Wow, it is dark out here!"

Their ears are alert. They take in the soft hum of the nighttime sounds. They hear some frogs singing nearby. Farther away, two screech owls communicate with each other. They listen for any sounds that might be deer.

"No deer sounds, yet," is what they hear from their ears.

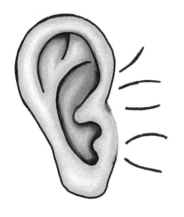

You might pause to
notice the sounds
around you right now.

Can you identify them?

They each take a deep breath
through their nose, sniffing the air.

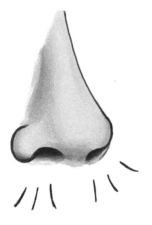

Are there any smells
where you are now?

Can you identify them?

"Nothing unusual in this air," they
hear from their noses.

Then they drop within themselves to listen to their gut sense. They each put one hand on their belly. "All safe!" they hear from their belly.

Hummah shows them safe like this.

Maybe your belly shows you safe in a different way.

Are there times you can think of where your belly acts upset, like it is afraid you are not safe?

Stryder squeezes Wendy's hand. This is his signal that he is ready to move and explore the backyard.

Wendy squeezes Stryder's hand back. She is ready too.

They drop hands. Wendy turns to her right. Stryder turns to his left. They both move quietly, like a deer would, into the yard.

Our bodies are always observing our environment. Wendy and Stryder have seen deer move many times.

It is easy for our bodies to imitate what we have paid attention to. Is there an animal you can imitate?

They each take about 10 steps.

Woosh!

Stamp!

Snort!

Stamp!

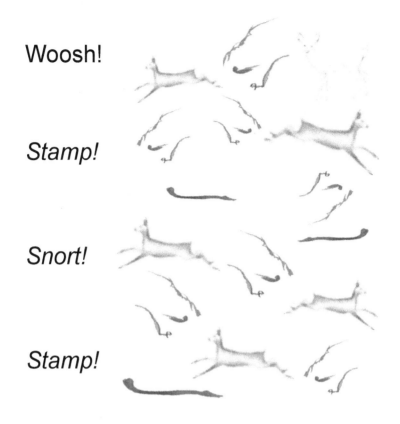

Wendy and Stryder hear movements and sounds they recognize as deer.

There are deer out here! And close by!

Both Wendy and Stryder stop to watch and listen.

The deer do not stay around. They turn and dash out of the yard. Wendy counts five dark shadows leap past her. From where Stryder is, he can only hear and sense them moving away.

"Wow, there were five deer here!" exclaims Wendy. "We could not see them or hear them. You just KNEW it from deep inside. You are amazing, Stryder! What a wonderful skill!"

Stryder stood still as he processed his own surprise. Then, as if he caught the energy of the deer, he suddenly moves! Stryder stamps his feet, snorts and begins running in a circle with glee.

Wendy laughs and joins him.

A light turns on in the house. It is
from Mama and Papa's bedroom.

Papa calls out the open window,
"Are you two outside?"

"Yes, Papa," calls back Stryder, "We found out when the deer are eating Mama's flowers."

"Oh, I would never have guessed!" chimes in Mama, "They eat in the middle of the night? No wonder Casey does not notice."

Hearing his name, Casey, their dog, stands up, shakes and wags his tail in the living room. "Woof! woof!" He wants them to know he is awake now too.

Stryder and Wendy move back toward the house. "You tell them," Wendy says.

Mama, Papa and Casey meet them in the kitchen.

Stryder tells his story. "I woke up and could not go back to sleep. When I checked inside, something in me said 'You were wondering when the deer are eating Mama's flowers. They are out there now.' Wendy was awake too. We went outside to check. We could not hear or see them. When we walked into the yard though, they were there. Wendy saw five of them running away."

"Isn't that an amazing skill, Mama and Papa?" Wendy rocks back and forth excitedly from her heels to toes. "I want to learn how to know things before I can see or hear them. What fun I could have!"

Have you ever woken up and had trouble going back to sleep?

Did you feel annoyed that you were awake?

Did you feel worried that you could not fall back asleep?

Maybe next time this happens, you could try this.

Pause and listen inside of yourself with curiosity.

Maybe your body has something to say that you did not yet know.

Could you make space for that possibility?

Ashamaya shows us here how we can make enough space for something annoyed (red), something worried (blue), and the something wanting our attention right now (green).

This green character sure looks like it has something fun to share!

Papa nods. "Wow, that is way cool buddy. I'm proud of you both for being curious enough to explore this further together. Our body wisdom reaches far. The more we pause to listen, the more we encourage our body to share what it knows. This is an adventure you can continue to build upon."

Mama smiles. "Papa's so right. Being able to hear our body wisdom is a skill that will be with you for life. I confess I am glad you were together. And what a surprise the deer visit us at 3:30am! They are early risers!"

Mama leans forward to give both Wendy and Stryder a hug. "Would you two be up for a graham cracker snack? A little treat can help us all wind down and go back to sleep.

Ashamaya often helps us nurture ourselves and others.

Wendy is still rocking back and forth on her tiptoes. Her eyes get big and she nods while looking at Stryder.

Stryder responds, "That would be nice, Mama. We got excited out there."

They each grab their water bottle from the counter. Mama spreads peanut butter on graham crackers. They sit down. As they pass the graham crackers around, the energy in the room slows. Each focuses their attention on enjoying this favorite family treat.

Mama's idea offers an opportunity to pause and listen within. Ashamaya helps her create soothing family time after some excitement.

Stryder and Wendy finish. You can tell they are getting sleepy. Yawning, they get up to put their water bottles back on the counter.

Stryder turns and says, "Thank you, everyone. I will not forget this."

Mama and Papa nod, smiling, as they follow their children upstairs to bed.

New Moon Walking

"Mama! Mama!" calls Wendy as
she runs toward the pottery
studio.

"Yes, Wendy, I am here." Mama
answers.

Wendy slows down as she turns the corner into mama's studio. Almost breathless, she says, "Did you know today is the New Moon Walk? Grammy said maybe I could come because it's Friday. It's a no school night!"

Mama smiles. "Well, yes, today is the day. I am sensing this would be fun for you."

Wendy jumps up and down. "Oh, more than fun, Mama. This is like a dream come true! The leaves are super thick on the trails right now."

"Indeed, leaves are everywhere!" says Mama. "Something about them makes this like a dream come true."

Wendy's eyes look toward the sky. "Oh, Mama, with fallen leaves everywhere, the trail will be that much harder to sense. Lynette has told me about this. She says fresh fallen leaves have taught her to see with her feet."

Mama is truly interested in what is beneath Wendy's excitement.

Ashamaya helps Mama create space for Wendy to feel safe and welcome to share more. And yes, there is more than we might guess.

Wendy pauses, looks down at her feet and sighs.

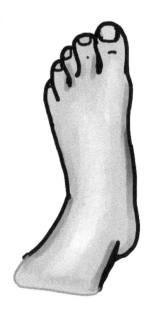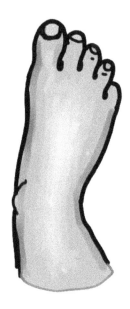

"Mama," she adds, "my feet DREAM of new moon walks! They can learn how to feel safe in the dark." Wendy leans toward her mom and drops her voice to a whisper: "Mama, if my feet could feel safe, they would do more than walk. They would dance in the dark!"

"Whoa!" Mama nods her head up and down in understanding. "I can hear how important this is to you. Yes, let's join Grammy for the New Moon Walk this evening."

Maybe you can pause and invite your feet to share with you how they feel: would they like to see in the dark?

Would they move differently if they had more experience?

What would help them feel safe to explore moving in the dark?

After dinner, Mama Dawn and Wendy walk hand in hand up the road. On their way, they wonder who will be there tonight. Wendy says, "I hope Lynette is coming! I will choose her as my forest buddy."

Mama replies, "Oh, good for you! Maybe Mina will be my buddy. Something in me is worried I will be slow or hurt myself. My eyes have very little practice adjusting to low-light situations."

Wendy squeezes Mama's hand. "Oh, we are both being so brave! What an adventure this will be! Thank you again for coming with me, Mama." Mama squeezes Wendy's hand back as they turn off the road toward the trailhead.

Grammy greets them with laughter and hugs. "Hooray! How wonderful that Mama Dawn and Wendy are here with us!"

Grampy steps up for hugs next. As he steps back, he looks into Mama's eyes. "Wow, Dawn, seeing you here is a surprise!"

Mama Dawn and Grampy connect with a hug and eye gaze using their Hummah powers.

"Oh, I know!" Mama Dawn replies. "I heard how important this is for Wendy. Papa Sam is playing fiddle at the Friday night music jam, or it's likely he would be here instead!"

Mama Mina steps up next. She reaches out to hold one of Dawn's hands in hers. "How perfect that you are here, Mama Dawn. I can be your forest buddy if you'd like. I can help you feel safe until your eyes adjust."

"Oh, thank you Mina!" says Dawn. "I was hoping you'd offer."

Wendy found Lynette. The two girls hold hands as well.

Grammy rings a bell that she pulls out of a bag. "Let's circle up! Dear ladies, thank you for joining Grampy and I for our monthly new moon walk. We have been doing this together for about 5 years. Every time our experience is fresh!"

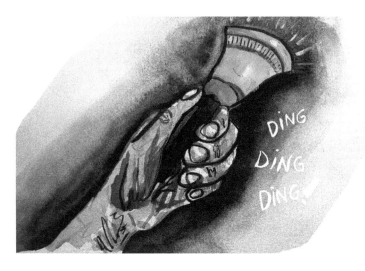

Grammy rings her bell!

Grammy pauses to listen within herself. "Yes, some new awareness comes each time. Since this walk is new for Dawn and Wendy, let's review our suggestions."

Grammy points to her eyes. "First, our eyes will have different comfort levels with the dark. Your eyes will communicate with you as you walk in the dark.

Be the listener to their unease.

Be the listener to their worries.

Night walks teach other parts of our body to help us see. As you walk and listen within, your eyes will adjust and relax. Invite this sense of safety in the dark. With practice, this sense gets stronger."

Ashamaya helps Grammy explain how to be a listener to our eyes.

Grammy points to her feet. "Second, keeping your attention with your eyes, expand your awareness to your feet. At other times, you could practice this barefoot. We wear shoes for this walk because there are rocky places on our route. Maybe someone else would like to share how your feet help you with this experience?"

Lynette raises her hand. "Yes, Grammy. For me, it is important to walk slowly. If I go slowly, it is like my eyes and feet together keep me safe. I am aware of what is below my foot as I bring it down. If my foot is not landing flat, I adjust it. My feet also tell me whether I am on the path. The path feels firmer than where I wander off the path a bit."

Grammy smiles. "Oh, how helpful Lynette! A slow pace will deepen this experience. The trail is wide enough to hold your buddy's hand."

Grampy chimes in, "Grammy will go first. I will go last. We will space ourselves 1 minute apart. It's getting darker. Are we ready?"

Wendy jumps up and down. "Yes! I'm so excited!"

Grammy starts walking.

Grampy drums a steady beat and leads them in a song that lasts 1 minute. It goes something like this:

"*Bring peace to the world.*
Bring love to your heart.
Bring joy to this day of life."*

Lynette and Wendy go next.
Mama's Mina and Dawn follow.
Grampy is last.

Grampy and Grammy chose a
wonderful path for this walk. This
trail follows along the Blue Ridge
Parkway. It is flat and wide. They
may get a glimpse of where they
are as car headlights pass by. The
walk begins in a field by their barn
and ends in an open space called

Smart View Overlook. For about 20 minutes between these spots, they walk through woods.

There is some initial chatter among the pairs as they walk through the field. The faint light here allows their eyes time to adjust.

A hush falls over each new moon walker as they enter the woods.

Ashamaya welcomes each walker.

As Wendy enters the woods, a point comes where she no longer sees shades of grey with her eyes. There is only blackness. Black in front of her. Black on each side. Both girls slow their movement.

Wendy feels Hummah move through her, turning on circuits in her skin, gut and feet. Wow!

~ Her eyes relax.

~ Her skin tells her there are trees on her sides.

~ Her gut sense reminds her that animals move with ease in the dark.

~ And there are eyes forming on Wendy's feet! She imagines tiny head lamps like antennas on both of her feet. They sense what is ahead.

Wendy also notices thoughts suggesting she could go back. They show her some favorite things she could be doing now, safe at home. She smiles toward these.

Wendy giggles with excitement. She squeezes Lynette's hand. With each step, they practice seeing with their feet. It feels like such an adventure!

The leaves crunch as they walk. Wendy practices listening with her feet to the texture of the ground. It is tricky, like Lynette said. The leaves form a cushion and hide the firmness of the trail.

They trip a bit sometimes. At one point, they hear a car coming up from behind them on the nearby

A picture of textures on the ground at Smart View Recreation Area in the fall.

Parkway. Lights from the car form shadows. It feels magical to watch the shadows of the car headlights dance in the woods.

At one point, Wendy hears her mama shriek several times from back behind them. It surprises her. She lets go of Lynette's hand and turns around to look backward. Bam! She falls down. Branches on the edge of the trail tangle around one of her feet. Lynette helps her up. Wendy tosses the branches farther into the woods. Now, they hear a shriek followed by both of their mamas laughing. Or maybe they are crying.

Lynette says, "Let's wait for them and find out what happened."

Wendy nods.

Once Lynette can hear their footsteps, she yells out, "Mama, Wendy and I are waiting here for you guys."

Mama Mina answers, "Oh good, sing so we can tell where you are."

Lynette starts Grampy's chant. Wendy joins in. As they sing, both mamas and Grampy join in. Within minutes, they are all together.

"Bring peace to the world.
Bring love to your heart.
*Bring joy to this day of life."**

Mama Dawn begins, "I'm sorry if I scared you girls. Something moved across the trail in front of us and I lost it. It felt like a possum, a raccoon, maybe even one of our cats. My legs froze while the rest of me was still moving forward and I went down fast. In fact, both Mina and I fell down! Mina's support and humor saved the situation!"

Mama Mina laughs. "We might still be there laughing if Grampy had not helped us get up. We are both fine."

Ashamaya smiles while gently holding fearful Sleuthin and frozen Hummah for Mama Dawn. Finding our sense of humor in moments like this helps the experience move forward in a positive way. This is easier for most of us when we have a supportive friend like Mina nearby.

"Oh, I am glad," says Wendy. She raises her arm in the air. "Grampy to the rescue!"

Grampy smiles. "We are almost at the overlook. I imagine Grammy will love to hear about our adventure." The ladies hear Grampy's hint that Grammy is waiting. They find their partner's hand, pause a moment to feel their feet, and begin moving again.

Grampy was right. Around the next bend, Wendy sees a shade of grey ahead. They are almost there! They also hear Grammy ringing her bell. Both Wendy and Lynette pick up their pace. Their ears and eyes feel more confidence in helping them now.

As they come out of the woods, Wendy and Lynette almost run to Grammy. Wendy says, "Grammy, my feet are growing eyes! Just baby eyes, but I can feel them. It's for real!"

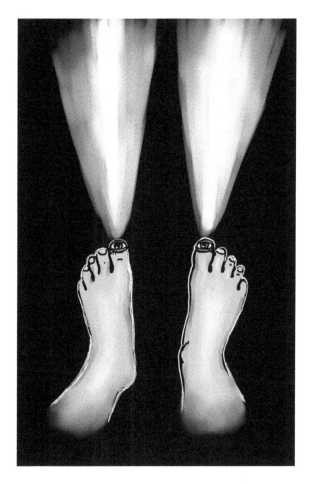

Wendy's feet-eyes!

Grammy smiles, "I am so happy for you Wendy! Keep practicing and your feet-eyes will get stronger and stronger."

Both Mamas and Grampy join them now. Grammy looks toward Mama Dawn, "How was the New Moon Walk for you, Dawn?"

Mama Dawn answers, "Well, I did not access the sense of eyes on my feet yet. My body found the entire experience a bit… hmm… what is the word… ahh… bewildering. Yes. Bewildering! Bewildering because I am not very skilled. Parts of me feel afraid and confused. I can tell I carry cultural beliefs that darkness is scary. I am also aware of mystery here to explore. Overall, I felt safe enough. I imagine these walks could help me feel comfortable with darkness in a variety of ways."

Grammy smiles. "Yes, I hear there is a lot that comes with 'Bewildering'. I agree moon walks are a gentle way for cultural beliefs about darkness to peek out at us. Today, I said hello to something in me that is concerned about the smells of darkness. It began as I took in the smell of decaying leaves. The smell is stronger where the leaves are deep. I can tell this is an old fear. Like you, I am aware of mystery here to explore."

Grammy pauses and looks up at the night sky. "Speaking of mystery, here is our treat. Grampy, maybe you can drum for us as we spend some time enjoying the expansive sky view this overlook offers us."

They all look up. Grampy drums softly. Awe and hush spread among them as they welcome the magic of dark sparkling sky.

*Music by Bob Grubel. (2008). "Bring Peace to the World". On *Red Ripe Apples* (CD).

The Blame Game

Papa lets out a deep sigh as he pours himself a cup of hot tea. He hopes to enjoy it outside on the porch. Before he heads out, he pauses and listens to the sounds in his home.

Levi's room is quiet. Oh, what a blessing! Levi played with Perla outside on her swing set this evening. He was already in his pajamas when Papa picked him up after playing music at the Friday night music jam. Levi fell asleep with just one bedtime song. How sweet!

Stryder's room is not as quiet. He is playing computer games with his friends online. Guessing from the intensity in Stryder's voice, Papa wonders if his team is close to finishing a goal. Game time ends at 8 pm on Friday evenings. Papa has five minutes to relax with his tea.

CRASH!

"MAAMAA! PAAPAA!"

Papa gets up and heads to
Stryder's room. He sees a chair
has fallen on the floor.

Papa stops in the doorway and
turns to his left. Stryder is standing
in front of his computer. His
shoulders are shaking. His hands
clenched tight at his sides.

Papa stays in the doorway,
shuffling so Stryder can hear he is
here. He does not enter the room.
He can sense Stryder needs
space.

"Dylan is an idiot. Look how angry I am! Help me not hurt the computer, Papa." says Stryder.

"Ah. Something in you is so angry!" Papa says. "Maybe we say hello to that. Hello something that got this angry." He moves into the room just enough to reach Stryder's bed. He pushes some pillows onto the floor.

Stryder turns toward him and narrows his eyes. "Are you suggesting a pillow fight?"

Papa raises his eyebrows. "It beats breaking your computer."

Stryder shakes his head and turns toward the pillows.

Notice how Papa accepts Stryder's anger. He even says maybe WE say hello to that.

Papa helps distract Stryder's focus from the computer and adds some lightness. Pillow fights are something playful they do together. This helps Stryder expand his awareness to more than Dylan.

Stryder bends down to grab one, then changes his mind. He picks up one foot and stomps it down near the pillows. "Argh! Idiot! I'm never playing with him again!" Stryder picks up the other foot and swings his arms now, too. "Never again." He continues one foot, then the other.

Stomp!
"Never
again."

Stomp!
"Never."

Stomp!
"Ever."

Stomp!
"Never."

Stomp!
"Ever."

Sleuthin is often involved when we feel anger or blame. This part of our brain likes to be in control. It can get very frustrated at whatever does not fit its beliefs.

Papa stands nearby. After a few minutes, Stryder lightens his stomp. Tears roll down his cheeks, and he begins jogging in place.

When we have an emotion that feels strong, a valuable skill is to acknowledge HOW BIG IT is. We acknowledge this directly to IT. If necessary, we find a safe way for the emotion to express HOW big IT is. Remember, this emotion is not all of you. Emotions are something in us looking for a way to release energy. Various movements, sounds, and tears can help our emotions express themselves.

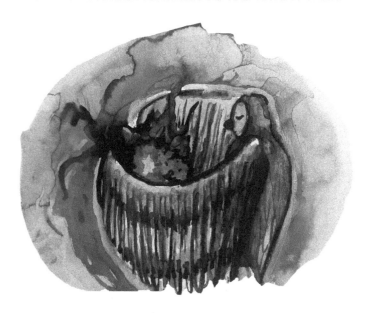

Ashamaya helps Papa step back and make space for Stryder's anger. This is important. If Papa gets angry at Stryder, now we have even more anger looking for a way to be acknowledged and express itself.

Papa takes the shift from stomping to jogging as a signal that Stryder has distanced himself from his anger.

"How 'bout we go outside together, Stryder," suggests Papa.

Stryder nods and follows Papa outside. Casey, their dog, gets up from resting on the porch and joins them. They walk on the road together. Papa lets Stryder choose the pace.

Every once in a while, Stryder stomps his feet and grumbles.

They get about halfway around the community circle. Stryder sighs and puts his hand on his head. "What a mess. I felt blame and anger toward Dylan and myself. Like a storm raging in me. I am feeling better. Thank you, Papa, for helping me move through it. I have a sense Sleuthin is getting his normal colors back."

Papa nods. "Ahh, yeah, the storm has passed."

They continue walking in silence. Papa notices Stryder's pace is slower now.

Stryder says, "I know you have taught me many times not to blame. It's still hard for me."

"I understand Stryder, I still catch myself blaming too," says Papa. "We use blaming often in our culture. It takes a lot of awareness and practice to choose something different."

They approach their house. Papa walks a pace behind Stryder. He is curious if Stryder will go into the house. Stryder keeps going.

While keeping up with Stryder, Papa tunes his ear toward Levi's room. Papa glimpses Levi's bedroom window partially open and does not hear his voice. He can tell the light is off. Papa senses Levi is sleeping just fine and turns his attention back to Stryder.

Ashamaya helps Papa with the Power of AND, awareness of both Levi and Stryder.

Stryder says, "It is that team thing again, Papa. It's so hard for me. I play to stay alive and win. Dylan plays differently from me. So many times I could not understand why he made a move. Dylan's choices often helped the other teams. Why was that? And, Papa, he is so slow at choices. I tried to give him space. Time ticked away! I had to yell his name to get him to do something. Ugh. So annoying."

Papa responds, "Hmm. You are holding space for a lot. Maybe it feels right to let these thoughts and memories know you really hear how hard this team thing is. It's so hard for you."

Sleuthin will often remind us to pay attention to the time on a clock. This can cause stress so that we find ourselves yelling and getting annoyed. With attention, we can teach ourselves to have a less stressful relationship with time.

Stryder nods. "Yeah, super hard."

They walk in silence.

Stryder sighs. "Papa, something in me wonders why I play team games. I cannot make people do it my way. I also don't want to. I get so confused. It is hard to not think my way is better. Something in me wants to try their ideas. Something wants to trust my choices. How do I know what is right? How do I ever enjoy being a team player?"

Papa smiles. "Oh Stryder, these are big questions many people wonder about all of their lives. I'll suggest that the answer lies within you, not outside of you. A key word might be 'team player'. If you continue to listen within as you are now, you will find your answers."

Stryder sighs and smiles back. "I get it. This is not just about team games, is it Papa?"

"It sounds bigger than team games to me, Stryder," says Papa.

Stryder nods.

Stryder's inner team is hopeful and forms a team huddle.

Papa notices Stryder's shoulders shift back, more balanced, like his normal stride. As they come around the loop with their house in view again, Casey runs ahead. They see Wendy and Mama approaching from the other direction. They hear Wendy's voice. She is talking excitedly about the New Moon Walk.

Papa slows down and touches Stryder's shoulder. "Are you ready for this?" He nods toward the girls.

Stryder smiles. "Yea, Papa, it will be a welcome change of pace. I can tell this whole team thing will take time. Thank you for helping me listen within. There is hope now, like I want to play again. I will apologize to Dylan sometime too."

As Wendy chatters, Stryder smiles to himself. One team game he always does well at is 'Walking Together'.

Appendix
Focusing

The relational skills our story characters practice is called Focusing. Focusing helps us pause for a moment and create space for new and unexpected possibilities in our awareness and understanding. It is also known as the essence of change; how a pattern or behavior becomes something different. These skills are accessible to everyone and are improved over time with practice. The International Focusing Institute supports individuals and groups in developing these skills. For more information, check out www.focusing.org.

Felt Sense Literacy

"We all agree that Focusing is a natural process. It is a capacity of every human being. Making an analogy with reading and writing, focusing is something everyone should be enabled to discover and develop. To view it along the lines of "literacy" places Focusing at the most basic level. It is something everyone can naturally have."

Marion Hendricks-Gendlin, Ph.D.
Felt Sense Literacy:
http://previous.focusing.org/literacy/index.htm

Neuroscience

Neuroscience is the study of our nervous system. Our nervous system is more complex than the entire universe yet discovered. It is involved in every aspect of our body. Our nervous system manages our behaviors. From how we feel, to what we know, how we breathe or move, all of our bodily systems. Our nervous system has a lot of responsibility for our well-being.

Focusing gives us the skills to understand the language of our nervous system. Body sensations, emotions, moods, images, words, gestures and movements are all ways our body speaks to us every day. A yawn is our body communicating 'something' to us. A thought is our mind communicating with us. Our body does not lie if we learn how to check back to see if we are understanding it correctly.

With the traditional way our brains are wired, most of our actions are reactions. With practice, we can change how we use our brain to make choices that feel more authentic and alive. We can heal cultural trauma and help humanity adapt to our ever-changing world. We can be the change we want to see around us.

Smart View Recreation Area Virginia, USA

The name Smart View refers to the long range, peaceful and colorful views here. This recreation area includes picnic grounds, restrooms, hiking trails and the Trail Cabin exhibit. The exhibit is a one room dwelling built in the early 1890s and moved here.

The land is a mix of moist woodland, hardwood forest and open fields. Native wildflowers such as chicory, asters, and clovers grow in the fields. Stones and large mossy rocks are abundant. There are several streams and one marshy area. A wide variety of birds visit, breed and live here. Deer, squirrels and chipmunks are easy to spot. Bear, opossum, skunk, turtles, snakes, salamanders and so much more also call this land home. Elevation: 2503 ft.

Smartview Village Map

Smartview Village Family Trees

Grampy grew up on this property. It is magical. When Grammy joined him, he took her first to the grove of old oak trees. The pair walk here daily and came to know these trees as family. When Grampy welcomed other families to live here, he invited them to walk the property, listen to the land and commit to join a family of trees here. Our map shows the tree each family chose and where they built their home. Symbols under the tree remind us of ways this family bonds with each other.

When you visit Smart View Recreation Area, an old log cabin is on the same site as the **Oak** Family tree on our map. Grampy & Grammy's home is much larger. It resembles farm homes you'll see along the Blue Ridge Parkway. It is white with wide covered porches. They often host Sunday brunch and music jams on their porch. Grammy picks baskets of food from the gardens for Grampy to cook with. When they are not hosting friends, they often visit them on Grampy's motorcycle.

Large lemon colored petals from Poplar tree flowers were covering the ground the day Sam, Dawn, Stryder and Wendy came to Smartview to choose their tree. The girls collected the petals. The guys pointed out how fast, straight and tall it grows. With this tree's majesty plus artistic leaves and petals, the **Poplar** tree felt like a match for their family. Shared time revolves around the arts and the outdoors. They all use bikes to get around. Someone from the family often joins Mama Dawn when she canoes on nearby Philpott Lake.

Doug is a master woodworker, and his favorite wood is maple. Mina, Terri and Lynette knew before they came to walk that their family tree would be **Maple**. They found plenty to fall in love with. The girls danced in circles, twisting and turning playfully like maple seeds falling to the ground. Terri challenged her family to walk across a maple that had fallen over a stream. Mina sang a poem about the beauty of red-orange-yellow maple leaves. This family shares a love for nature and wildlife. They invite birds in close to their home. They like to look for and create special spaces to meditate in nature at Smartview.

As a newly blended family, Aunt Betty, Amber and Perla took several visits to choose their tree. They hugged this tree and that. Aunt Betty's favorite childhood dresser, her oldest piece of furniture, is made from cherry wood. Dangling white blossoms cover the black cherry trees in late spring. Their fruit feeds a wide variety of birds and other wildlife. Perla pointed out cherries go with good things like ice cream sundaes, and they all cheered 'Yes'! The **Cherry** Family plays a board game to relax after dinner. They all enjoy cooling off with a swim at the pond on hot summer days.

A Peek at the Poplar Family!

Together, they enjoy biking, camping, art, singing, and music. Mama Dawn and Papa Sam learned Focusing shortly before Stryder was born so that they could raise their kids with these skills. They are a typical busy family and feel blessed to be using Focusing as a way of life in community with others.

Age 38
Mama Dawn is a social butterfly, involved in helping others in the community. She works as an artisan potter. Her hobbies are Qi-gong, biking, kayaking, and gardening.

Age 37
Papa Sam is the founder of a local nonprofit business dedicated to raising awareness about mindfulness skills. His hobbies are walking with Casey, his dog, video games, and playing fiddle at Friday night jams in Floyd.

Age 11

Stryder likes to move and runs, bikes or plays basketball almost every day. One of his goals is to join a local track team. Stryder feels movement helps him be more attentive when he is sitting to read or play a video game.

Age 8

Wendy is adaptable and likes to keep her options open. She loves to draw and is already a talented artist. Since moving here, her new hobby is plants, learning about them, and spending time learning to communicate with them.

Age 4
Levi does not talk much. He is often sensitive, showing off one moment, and closing down the next. Levi is Mama Dawn's nephew who recently joined the family. It's not clear how long he will be here. His parents live in a big city and travel often for their jobs. They hope Levi will thrive more in this environment. He loves birds and imitates bird sounds beautifully.

Age 3
Casey lives in adoration of her family. She is quite attentive to Papa Sam for walks, one-on-one time, and treats. She is also quite happy that Levi is here. She often sits near him as he plays in a sunny rock patch outside the home.

Introducing our Smartview Stories Team!

Sandy & Inge exploring at Smart View Recreation Area

Sandy Jahmi Burg, certified Focusing trainer with The International Focusing Institute, is the primary author and coordinator of this project. You might guess she is a neuroscience geek! Sandy has experience in permaculture design and has lived in small intentional communities since 2005. Her three children inspired her interest in processing styles.

Inge Terrill is a Focuser, educator, editor, wellness coach, biologist, and Smartview co-creator extraordinaire. She is currently pursuing Certification in Focusing. Inge is most familiar with the land where Smartview Stories take place. This was a favorite nature spot of her family's as her two daughters were growing up.

Our Illustrators!

Creator of our Inner Companions, Nomi Miller is a believer in magic and the power of words. She likes to draw, dance, sing, be silly, and do nothing at all. Nomi lives in a garden colony in Denmark with her son Ruben.

Creator of the deer acrylics, Molly Gutiérrez lives with her husband, Sam, and their house full of fur babies in Roanoke, Virginia. She enjoys whipping up yummy things in the kitchen, digging in the dirt, healing through mind and body modalities, and discovering new depths through drawing.

Smartview Stories™ would not be where they are without all of the love the Smartview team breathes into this project!

Creator of our People, Aaron Staengl is an artist and Ayurvedic practitioner with a regular meditation and yoga practice. His company Ayurvedaposters has an international presence. He lives in the Blue Ridge mountains and enjoys spending time with his two year old son.

Creator of our Map, Renee La Roi is an American Canadian, and a long time Focuser, based in Vancouver, Canada.
She is also a certified Focusing professional, graphic artist and yogi. She loves to travel & bike & practice yoga outside --- she is a big dreamer.

CPSIA information can be obtained
at www.ICGtesting.com
Printed in the USA
BVHW062145070123
655773BV00003B/15